DIABETI
CHOLESTE... ...OKBOOK

The complete guide to low cholesterol cooking with delicious Heart-Healthy Diabetic recipes to manage diabetes and heart disease.

DR. Joseph C. Jones

CONTENTS

5 |Diabetics and high cholesterol cookbook

INTRODUCTION:

Sarah had always loved her buttered toast and creamy pasta, but lately, those indulgences came with a side of worry. The doctor's words echoed in her ears: "Type 2 diabetes and high cholesterol, Sarah. We need to make some changes."

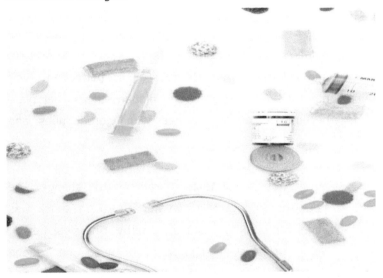

Feeling overwhelmed, Sarah sank into her couch, a tub of ice cream calling her name. But then, a memory flickered – her grandma's kitchen, filled with the aroma of herbs and spices, not store-bought sauces. Grandma lived a long, healthy life, and it wasn't just genes – it was her food!

Determined, Sarah embarked on a culinary adventure. She traded white bread for whole wheat, its nutty flavor surprisingly satisfying.

Olive oil replaced butter, bringing a peppery kick to her dishes.
Salmon, once reserved for special occasions, became a regular, thanks to its heart-healthy fats.

Experimentation became her game. She discovered hidden gems like quinoa, a fluffy grain rich in protein, and colorful vegetables roasted to perfection, their natural sweetness replacing hidden sugars. Her plate became a canvas, painted with vibrant hues and textures.

But it wasn't just taste. Sarah felt the change. The sluggishness that followed her afternoon snack was gone, replaced by sustained energy. She slept better, woke up feeling lighter, and even her mood brightened. Food wasn't just fuel; it was medicine, and she was its chef.

Challenges arose.
Birthday cake at her friend's party? She opted for a smaller slice and savored the flavor instead of mindlessly indulging.

Cravings for her old favorites? She found healthier alternatives – a creamy avocado spread instead of mayo, dark chocolate with nuts for a sweet fix.

Slowly, the numbers on the doctor's report started to shift. Her blood sugar stabilized; her cholesterol dipped. But the victory wasn't just medical; it was personal. Sarah had taken control of her health, not through deprivation, but through discovery.

One day, while whipping up a batch of her now-famous lentil soup for her family, Sarah realized she wasn't just cooking; she was wearing a new story. A story where delicious food and vibrant health danced hand-in-hand. It was a story she was excited to share, not just with her family, but with the world.

And so, Sarah, the once intimidated cook, became Sarah, the recipe developer, the blogger, the author of "The Flavorful Flip: Cooking for Diabetes and a Healthy Heart." Her story, filled with simple swaps and delicious triumphs, became an inspiration to many, proving that good health and good food could be a beautiful duet on anyone's plate. And it all started with a decision, a memory, and a leap of faith into the kitchen.

Understanding the Interplay: Diabetes, Cholesterol, and Your Diet

Navigating both diabetes and high cholesterol can feel like a complex dance, but understanding the connection between your diet and these conditions empowers you to take control of your health. Let's break down the key players and how your food choices influence them:

Diabetes:

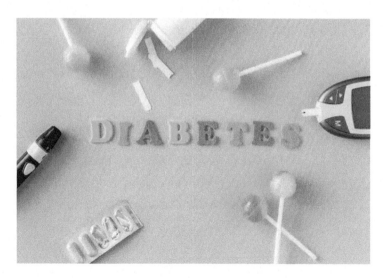

Blood Sugar: Glucose, a type of sugar, is your body's fuel. In diabetes, your body struggles to regulate blood sugar levels, leading to spikes after meals.

Carbohydrates: These break down into glucose, impacting your blood sugar.

Refined carbs like white bread and sugary drinks cause rapid sugar spikes, while complex carbs like whole grains offer slower, steadier release.

Cholesterol:

LDL ("bad") cholesterol: This builds up in arteries, increasing your risk of heart disease. Saturated and trans fats from fried foods, fatty meats, and processed snacks contribute to high LDL.

HDL ("good") cholesterol: This removes LDL from arteries, protecting your heart. Healthy fats like those in avocado, nuts, and olive oil can raise HDL levels.

The Interplay:

Inflammation: Both diabetes and high cholesterol are linked to inflammation, which can worsen both conditions. Eating a diet rich in fruits, vegetables, and fiber can help reduce inflammation.

Insulin Resistance: In type 2 diabetes, your body becomes less responsive to insulin, the hormone that helps cells absorb blood sugar. Choosing low-glycemic index foods (those that slowly raise blood sugar) can improve insulin sensitivity.

Your Dietary Toolkit:

Low-Carb Focus: While not magic, prioritizing low-carb options like vegetables, lean protein, and whole grains helps manage blood sugar. Limiting refined carbs and sugary drinks is key.

Healthy Fat Choices: Swap saturated and trans fats for unsaturated fats like those from olive oil, nuts, and avocados. These support heart health and can even improve insulin sensitivity.

Fiber Power: Include fiber-rich foods like fruits, vegetables, and whole grains in your diet. Fiber slows digestion, promoting steadier blood sugar and cholesterol levels.

Portion Control: Be mindful of serving sizes, even with healthy foods. Smaller, more frequent meals can help manage blood sugar and weight.

Navigating the Kitchen with Confidence: Your Guide to This Cookbook

Welcome to your personalized roadmap to delicious and nutritious meals that cater to both your diabetes and high cholesterol management!

This cookbook isn't just a collection of recipes; it's your empowering companion in the kitchen, guiding you towards culinary adventures free from fear and limitations.

Understanding Your Dietary Duo:

Before we dive into the world of flavor, let's talk about the two conditions we're managing: diabetes and high cholesterol.

While they might seem like separate challenges, understanding their connection to your diet is key to making informed choices.

Diabetes: Remember, your body struggles to regulate blood sugar levels. Refined carbohydrates and sugary treats lead to spikes, so we'll focus on low-carb options with gradual sugar release.

High Cholesterol: We want to keep "bad" LDL cholesterol in check and boost "good" HDL cholesterol. This means limiting saturated and trans fats while embracing healthy fats from sources like avocados and nuts.

Your Confidence-Building Kit:

This cookbook is packed with tools to make you feel comfortable and capable in the kitchen:

Simple-to-follow recipes: Clear instructions and familiar steps ensure smooth sailing, even for novice cooks.

Substitution suggestions: Don't have an ingredient? No worries! We offer alternatives to fit your pantry and preferences.

Nutritional information: Know exactly what's on your plate with detailed breakdowns of carbs, fiber, and fat content.

Tips and tricks: Learn about smart ingredient choices, cooking techniques, and meal planning strategies.

Embracing a Flavorful Future:

Forget bland, flavorless food!

This cookbook explodes with taste, proving that healthy can be exciting and delicious. Expect:

Breakfasts that kickstart your day: Fluffy pancakes with hidden veggies, savory egg scrambles with heart-healthy fats, and protein-packed smoothies.

Lunchtime creations that satisfy: Colorful salads with whole-wheat croutons, flavorful lentil soups, and satisfying quinoa bowls packed with veggies and lean protein.

Dinnertime feasts that bring everyone together: Baked salmon with roasted vegetables, slow-cooker dinners for effortless meals, and vegetarian options that burst with flavor.

Sweet treats that don't spike your sugar: No-bake energy bites, guilt-free muffins, and decadent dark chocolate desserts, all crafted with diabetes-friendly ingredients.

Remember:

Small changes matter: Start with one recipe at a time and gradually integrate new habits into your routine.

Cooking is a journey: Don't be afraid to experiment, adjust flavors, and personalize dishes to your liking.

Celebrate your successes: Every healthy meal cooked is a victory. Enjoy the process, **<u>savor the flavors, and nourish your body with confidence!</u>**

With this cookbook as your guide, you're empowered to create a kitchen filled with deliciousness, well-being, and the joy of cooking.

So, grab your apron, ignite your confidence, and let's get cooking!

Building a Foundation for Success: Essential Tips and Tools

Managing both diabetes and high cholesterol might seem like a daunting task, but fear not! By building a strong foundation in your kitchen, you can create delicious, nutritious meals that support your health goals. Here are some essential tips and tools to get you started:

Pantry Staples:

Low-carb grains: Stock up on quinoa, brown rice, whole-wheat pasta, and whole-wheat bread for sustained energy and fiber.

Lean protein sources: Chicken breast, fish, beans, lentils, and tofu provide essential nutrients without excessive saturated fat.

Healthy fats: Olive oil, avocado oil, nuts, and seeds offer good fats that support heart health.

Non-starchy vegetables: Fill your fridge with an array of colorful veggies like broccoli, spinach, carrots, peppers, and cauliflower for vitamins, minerals, and fiber.

Flavorful spices and herbs: Ditch the salt shaker and explore herbs like rosemary, thyme, and oregano, and spices like turmeric, chili powder, and cinnamon for vibrant, low-sodium flavor.

Cooking Tools:

Air fryer: This versatile tool helps you reduce fat intake while achieving crispy textures on protein and vegetables.

Blender/food processor: Whiz up smoothies, dips, dressings, and sauces for effortless meal prep and healthy additions.

Slow cooker: Perfect for creating wholesome, low-effort meals that simmer while you're busy.

Spiralizer: Transform vegetables like zucchini and sweet potatoes into noodle-like substitutes for lower-carb pasta alternatives.

Measuring cups and spoons: Accuracy is key, especially when managing portions and carbohydrate intake.

Planning and Organization:

Meal planning: Plan your meals and snacks for the week to avoid unhealthy decisions when hunger strikes. Utilize online resources or create your own plan using diabetes-friendly cookbooks and websites.

Read food labels: Be mindful of serving sizes, carbohydrate content, and hidden sugars and fats. Choose options lower in saturated and trans fats and added sugars.

Portion control: Use smaller plates and bowls to encourage mindful eating and prevent overindulging.

Stay hydrated: Water is your best friend! Eight glasses should be consumed daily to maintain your body in peak condition.

Additional Tips:

Don't go it alone: Seek support from a registered dietitian who can personalize your dietary plan and offer guidance.

Get moving: Regular physical activity plays a crucial role in managing both diabetes and heart health.

Celebrate small wins: Recognize and reward yourself for making healthy choices, no matter how small they seem.

Remember, consistency is key!

By incorporating these tips and tools into your routine, you'll build a solid foundation for a healthier, happier you. You've got this!

Foods to Avoid:

High-Carb:

Refined grains and starches: White bread, pasta, pastries, crackers, white rice, processed breakfast cereals

Sugary drinks: Soda, juice, sweetened coffee drinks, sports drinks

Dried fruits: Contain concentrated sugars

Starchy vegetables: Potatoes, corn, peas, beets

Sweet fruits: Mango, grapes, pineapple, bananas

High Saturated and Trans Fats:

Fatty meats: red meat, processed meats like sausage and bacon, organ meats

High-fat dairy products: Full-fat milk, cheese, butter, ice cream

Fried foods: Fried chicken, French fries, onion rings, commercially fried snacks

Baked goods: Cakes, cookies, pastries, croissants

Processed foods: Frozen meals, instant noodles, packaged snacks

Other:

Alcohol: Can affect blood sugar control and contribute to weight gain

Added sugars: Candy, chocolate bars, sugary yogurts, condiments with added sugar

Foods to Include:

Low-Carb and High-Fiber:

Non-starchy vegetables: Leafy greens, broccoli, cauliflower, peppers, asparagus, zucchini, mushrooms

Low-carb fruits: Berries, avocados, citrus fruits

Whole grains: Quinoa, brown rice, rolled oats, whole-wheat bread (in moderation)

Legumes: Beans, lentils, peas

Nuts and seeds: Almonds, walnuts, chia seeds, flaxseeds

Healthy Fats:

Unsaturated fats: Olive oil, avocado oil, canola oil, fatty fish (salmon, tuna)

Nuts and seeds: Almonds, walnuts, chia seeds, flaxseeds

Avocados: Rich in healthy fats, fiber, and potassium

Lean Protein:

Skinless chicken and turkey breast
Fish and seafood: Salmon, tuna, shrimp, cod
Eggs: A good source of protein and healthy fats
Plant-based protein: Tofu, tempeh, lentils, beans

Other:

Water: The best beverage for hydration
Unsweetened herbal teas and coffee: Enjoy in moderation
Spices and herbs: Add flavor without additional calories

CHAPTER 1:

Breakfast Delights:

Scrambled Eggs with Smoked Salmon and Avocado

Ingredients:

- 4 large eggs
- 100g smoked salmon, sliced
- 1 ripe avocado, sliced
- Salt and pepper to taste
- Fresh dill for garnish (optional)

Preparation Method:

- After cracking the eggs into a bowl, thoroughly whisk them together.
- Add little pepper and salt for seasoning.

- Pour the whisked eggs into a nonstick skillet and cook it over medium heat.
- Using a spatula, gently scramble the eggs until they are cooked to your desired consistency.
- Divide the scrambled eggs onto serving plates.
- Top each plate with slices of smoked salmon and avocado.
- Garnish with fresh dill, if desired.
- Serve immediately and enjoy!

Serving Size: 2 servings

Nutritional Information (per serving):

Calories: 290

Total Fat: 20g

Saturated Fat: 4g

Cholesterol: 380mg

Sodium: 450mg

Total Carbohydrates: 4g

Dietary Fiber: 3g

Sugars: 0g

Protein: 24g

Chia Pudding with Berries and Nuts

Ingredients:

- 1/4 cup chia seeds
- 1 cup unsweetened almond milk
- 1/2 cup mixed berries (strawberries, blueberries, raspberries)
- 2 tablespoons chopped nuts (almonds, walnuts, pecans)

Preparation Method:

- In a bowl, mix the chia seeds and almond milk until well combined.
- Cover the bowl and refrigerate for at least 2 hours or overnight, allowing the chia seeds to absorb the liquid and thicken into a pudding-like consistency.
- Once the chia pudding has set, divide it into serving bowls.

- Top each bowl with mixed berries and chopped nuts.
- Serve chilled and enjoy!

Serving Size: 2 servings

Nutritional Information (per serving):

Calories: 200

Total Fat: 13g

Saturated Fat: 1g

Cholesterol: 0mg

Sodium: 80mg

Total Carbohydrates: 18g

Dietary Fiber: 12g

Sugars: 2g

Protein: 7g

Whole-Wheat Pancakes with Berries and Greek Yogurt

Ingredients:

- 1 cup whole-wheat flour
- 1 tablespoon baking powder
- 1/4 teaspoon salt

- 1 tablespoon honey or maple syrup
- 1 cup unsweetened almond milk
- 1 large egg
- One tablespoon of heated coconut oil or olive oil
- Mixed berries for topping (strawberries, blueberries, raspberries)
- Greek yogurt for topping

Preparation Method:

- Combine the whole-wheat flour, baking powder, and salt in a large mixing dish.
- Mix the egg, almond milk, melted coconut oil, honey or maple syrup, and olive oil thoroughly in a separate bowl.
- Mixing until well mixed, pour the wet components into the dry ingredients. Take caution not to overmix; some lumps are acceptable.
- Grease a non-stick skillet or griddle with cooking spray or extra oil and heat it over medium heat.
- For each pancake, add approximately 1/4 cup of batter to the skillet.
- Cook the pancake until bubbles appear on its surface, then turn it over and continue cooking it until the second side is golden brown.
- Proceed with the leftover batter.

- Top the pancakes with Greek yogurt and a mixture of fruit.
- Enjoy warm!

Serving Size: 2 servings (about 6 pancakes)

Nutritional Information (per serving):

Calories: 350

Total Fat: 11g

Saturated Fat: 2g

Cholesterol: 55mg

Sodium: 620mg

Total Carbohydrates: 53g

Dietary Fiber: 8g

Sugars: 11g

Protein: 13g

Omelets with Spinach, Feta, and Tomato

Ingredients:

- 4 large eggs
- 1 cup fresh spinach leaves, chopped
- 1/4 cup crumbled feta cheese

- 1 small tomato, diced
- Salt and pepper to taste
- Cooking spray or olive oil for greasing the skillet

Preparation Method:

- Beat the eggs thoroughly with a whisk in a bowl. Add little pepper and salt for seasoning.
- A non-stick skillet should be gently oiled with cooking spray or olive oil before being heated over medium heat.
- Pour the beaten eggs into the skillet, tilting to spread evenly.
- Cook until the edges of the omelet begin to set, then use a spatula to gently lift and fold the omelet in half.
- Sprinkle the chopped spinach, crumbled feta cheese, and diced tomato over one half of the omelet.
- Cook for another minute or until the cheese starts to melt.
- Carefully slide the omelet onto a plate and fold it in half.
- Serve hot and enjoy!

Serving Size: 1 serving

Nutritional Information (per serving):

Calories: 260

Total Fat: 18g

Saturated Fat: 7g

Cholesterol: 380mg

Sodium: 560mg

Total Carbohydrates: 6g

Dietary Fiber: 2g

Sugars: 3g

Protein: 19g

Smoothie Bowl with Spinach, Banana, and Almond Milk

Ingredients:

1 ripe banana, frozen

1 cup fresh spinach leaves

1/2 cup unsweetened almond milk

1/4 cup Greek yogurt

1 tablespoon almond butter or peanut butter

Toppings: Sliced banana, berries, granola, chia seeds, shredded coconut (optional)

Preparation Method:

- In a blender, combine the frozen banana, fresh spinach leaves, almond milk, Greek yogurt, and almond butter or peanut butter.
- If additional almond milk is required to get the appropriate accuracy, blend until creamy and smooth.
- Pour the smoothie into a bowl.
- Arrange the toppings on top of the smoothie bowl as desired.
- Serve immediately and enjoy!

Serving Size: 1 serving

Nutritional Information (per serving):

Calories: 300

Total Fat: 12g

Saturated Fat: 1g

Cholesterol: 5mg

Sodium: 160mg

Total Carbohydrates: 43g

Dietary Fiber: 9g

Sugars: 21g

Protein: 11g

Oatmeal with Chia Seeds and Sliced Almonds:

Ingredients:
- 1/2 cup rolled oats (whole grain)
- 1 cup unsweetened almond milk
- 1 tablespoon chia seeds
- 1 tablespoon sliced almonds
- Cinnamon (optional)
- Natural sweetener (Stevia, erythritol, or monk fruit extract), to taste

Preparation Method:
- In a small saucepan, bring the almond milk to a simmer over medium heat.
- Stir in the rolled oats and chia seeds.
- Cook, stirring occasionally, for about 5-7 minutes or until the oats are cooked and the mixture has thickened.
- Remove from heat and let it sit for a minute.
- Sweeten with natural sweetener if desired, and sprinkle with sliced almonds and cinnamon.
- Serve warm and enjoy!

Serving Size: 1 serving

Nutritional Information (per serving):

Calories: 250
Total Fat: 9g
Saturated Fat: 1g
Cholesterol: 0mg
Sodium: 80mg
Total Carbohydrates: 35g
Dietary Fiber: 8g
Sugars: 1g
Protein: 8g

Avocado Toast with Scrambled Eggs:

Ingredients:
- 1 slice whole grain bread (low-carb if available)
- 1/2 avocado, mashed
- 2 eggs, scrambled
- Salt and pepper, to taste
- Chopped fresh herbs (optional)

Preparation Method:
- Toast the slice of whole grain bread.
- Using a fork, evenly distribute the mashed avocado.

- Top with scrambled eggs.
- Season with salt, pepper, and chopped fresh herbs if desired.
- Serve immediately and enjoy!

Serving Size: 1 serving
Nutritional Information (per serving):
Calories: 300
Total Fat: 18g
Saturated Fat: 4g
Cholesterol: 370mg
Sodium: 280mg
Total Carbohydrates: 20g
Dietary Fiber: 7g
Sugars: 2g
Protein: 17g

Baked Egg Muffins with Vegetables:

Ingredients:
- 4 eggs
- 1/4 cup chopped bell peppers
- 1/4 cup chopped spinach
- 1/4 cup diced tomatoes
- Salt and pepper, to taste
- To grease the muffin, pan, use cooking spray or olive oil.

Preparation Method:

- Preheat the oven to 350°F (175°C) and lightly grease a muffin tin.
- In a mixing bowl, whisk together the eggs.
- Stir in the chopped bell peppers, spinach, tomatoes, salt, and pepper.
- Pour the egg mixture evenly into the muffin tin compartments.
- Bake for 20-25 minutes, or until the egg muffins are set and lightly golden.
- Take out of the oven and allow it to cool down a little before serving.
- Enjoy warm or refrigerate for later use.

Serving Size: 2 muffins
Nutritional Information (per serving):
Calories: 150
Total Fat: 9g
Saturated Fat: 3g
Cholesterol: 370mg
Sodium: 240mg
Total Carbohydrates: 4g
Dietary Fiber: 1g
Sugars: 2g
Protein: 12g

Chia Seed Pancakes:

Ingredients:

- 2 tablespoons chia seeds
- 1/4 cup almond flour
- 2 eggs
- 1/4 cup unsweetened almond milk
- 1/2 teaspoon baking powder
- 1/2 teaspoon vanilla extract
- Natural sweetener (Stevia, erythritol, or monk fruit extract), to taste
- Cooking spray or olive oil for greasing pan

Preparation Method:

- In a mixing bowl, combine the chia seeds, almond flour, eggs, almond milk, baking powder, vanilla extract, and natural sweetener.
- Let the batter sit for 5-10 minutes to allow the chia seeds to absorb the liquid and thicken.
- Heat a non-stick skillet or griddle over medium heat and lightly grease with cooking spray or olive oil.
- Pour the pancake batter onto the skillet, using about 2 tablespoons for each pancake.
- Cook for 2-3 minutes on each side, or until golden brown and cooked through.
- Serve warm with toppings of your choice, such as fresh berries or a dollop of Greek yogurt.

Serving Size: 2 pancakes

Nutritional Information (per serving):
Calories: 220
Total Fat: 15g
Saturated Fat: 2g
Cholesterol: 180mg
Sodium: 170mg
Total Carbohydrates: 10g
Dietary Fiber: 6g
Sugars: 1g
Protein: 12g

Breakfast Tacos with Scrambled Eggs, Black Beans, and Salsa:

Ingredients:
- 2 eggs, scrambled
- 1/4 cup black beans, drained and rinsed
- 2 small whole grain tortillas (low-carb if available)
- 2 tablespoons salsa
- Fresh cilantro, chopped (optional)
- Lime wedges (optional)

Preparation Method:
- Heat the black beans in a small saucepan over medium heat until warmed through.
- Use a dry skillet or the microwave to reheat the tortillas.

- Spoon evenly between the tortillas the black beans and beaten eggs.
- If desired, sprinkle chopped cilantro and salsa on top.
- For added taste, present lime wedges beside the dish.

Serving Size: 1 serving (2 tacos)
Nutritional Information (per serving):
Calories: 300
Total Fat: 10g
Saturated Fat: 2g
Cholesterol: 340mg
Sodium: 430mg
Total Carbohydrates: 30g
Dietary Fiber: 9g
Sugars: 2g
Protein: 20g

CHAPTER 2:

Lunchtime Creations:

Salmon Salad with Quinoa and Roasted Vegetables

Ingredients:

2 salmon fillets

1 cup cooked quinoa

2 cups mixed greens (spinach, kale, arugula)

1 cup assorted roasted vegetables (bell peppers, zucchini, cherry tomatoes)

2 tablespoons olive oil

1 tablespoon lemon juice

Salt and pepper to taste

Fresh herbs for garnish (optional)

Preparation Method:

- Preheat the oven to 400°F (200°C). Arrange the salmon fillets onto a parchment paper-lined baking sheet.
- Add a drizzle of lemon juice, olive oil, salt, and pepper.
- Bake the salmon for a minimum of twelve to fifteen minutes, or until it is thoroughly cooked.
- In a large bowl, combine the cooked quinoa, mixed greens, and roasted vegetables.
- Divide the salad mixture onto plates and top each with a cooked salmon fillet.
- Garnish with fresh herbs if desired.
- Serve immediately and enjoy!

Serving Size: 2 servings

Nutritional Information (per serving):

Calories: 400

Total Fat: 20g

Saturated Fat: 3g

Cholesterol: 60mg

Sodium: 300mg

Total Carbohydrates: 25g

Dietary Fiber: 5g

Sugars: 3g

Protein: 30g

Lentil Soup with Whole-Wheat Bread

Ingredients:

- 1 cup dry green lentils, rinsed
- 4 cups low-sodium vegetable broth
- 1 onion, chopped
- 2 carrots, diced
- 2 celery stalks, diced
- 2 cloves garlic, minced
- 1 teaspoon dried thyme
- 1 bay leaf
- Salt and pepper to taste
- 2 slices whole-wheat bread
- Fresh parsley for garnish (optional)

Preparation Method:

- In a large pot, combine the lentils, vegetable broth, onion, carrots, celery, garlic, thyme, and bay leaf. Bring to a boil, then reduce the heat to low and simmer for 25-30 minutes, or until the lentils are tender.

- After taking out the bay leaf, add pepper and salt according to your liking in the soup.
- Toast the whole-wheat bread slices until golden brown.
- Ladle the lentil soup into bowls and serve with the toasted whole-wheat bread.
- Garnish with fresh parsley if desired.
- Serve hot and enjoy!

Serving Size: 4 servings

Nutritional Information (per serving):

Calories: 250

Total Fat: 2g

Saturated Fat: 0g

Cholesterol: 0mg

Sodium: 400mg

Total Carbohydrates: 45g

Dietary Fiber: 12g

Sugars: 5g

Protein: 14g

Chicken Caesar Salad with Greek Yogurt Dressing

Ingredients:

- 2 boneless, skinless chicken breasts
- 4 cups romaine lettuce, chopped
- 1/4 cup cherry tomatoes, halved
- 2 tablespoons grated Parmesan cheese
- 1/4 cup Greek yogurt
- 1 tablespoon lemon juice
- 1 clove garlic, minced
- 1 teaspoon Dijon mustard
- Salt and pepper to taste
- Whole-wheat croutons (optional)

Preparation Method:

- Season the chicken breasts with salt and pepper.
- Heat a non-stick skillet over medium heat and cook the chicken breasts for 6-8 minutes per side, or until cooked through.

- Allow the chicken to cool, then slice into strips.
- In a small bowl, whisk together the Greek yogurt, lemon juice, minced garlic, Dijon mustard, salt, and pepper to make the dressing.
- In a large bowl, toss the chopped romaine lettuce with the sliced chicken breast, cherry tomatoes, and grated Parmesan cheese.
- Drizzle the Greek yogurt dressing over the salad and toss to coat evenly.
- Divide the salad onto plates and garnish with whole-wheat croutons if desired.
- Serve immediately and enjoy!

Serving Size: 2 servings

Nutritional Information (per serving):

Calories: 300

Total Fat: 8g

Saturated Fat: 2g

Cholesterol: 80mg

Sodium: 400mg

Total Carbohydrates: 10g

Dietary Fiber: 3g

Sugars: 4g

Protein: 40g

Black Bean Burgers on Whole-Wheat Buns with Sweet Potato Fries

Ingredients:

- One 15-oz can have rinsed and drained black beans1/2 cup cooked quinoa
- 1/4 cup finely chopped onion
- 1 clove garlic, minced
- 1 teaspoon ground cumin
- 1/2 teaspoon paprika
- Salt and pepper to taste
- 2 whole-wheat burger buns
- Lettuce leaves and sliced tomatoes for garnish
- 1 medium sweet potato, cut into fries
- 1 tablespoon olive oil
- 1/2 teaspoon garlic powder
- 1/2 teaspoon paprika
- Salt and pepper to taste

Preparation Method:

- Preheat the oven to 400°F (200°C). Line a baking sheet with parchment paper.
- In a large bowl, mash the black beans with a fork until mostly smooth.
- Add the cooked quinoa, chopped onion, minced garlic, ground cumin, paprika, salt, and pepper to the mashed black beans.
- Mix until well combined.
- Divide the black bean mixture into 2 portions and shape each portion into a patty.
- Place the black bean patties on the prepared baking sheet and bake in the preheated oven for 20-25 minutes, flipping halfway through, until the patties are firm and golden brown.
- While the patties are baking, prepare the sweet potato fries.
- In a bowl, toss the sweet potato fries with olive oil, garlic powder, paprika, salt, and pepper until evenly coated. Spread the fries in a single layer on a separate baking sheet lined with parchment paper.
- Bake the sweet potato fries in the preheated oven for 20-25 minutes, flipping halfway through, until crispy and golden brown.
- Toast the whole-wheat burger buns if desired.

- Assemble the black bean burgers by placing each patty on a bun and topping with lettuce leaves and sliced tomatoes.
- Put some sweet potato fries on the side and serve.
- Serve hot and enjoy!

Serving Size: 2 servings

Nutritional Information (per serving):

Calories: 450

Total Fat: 10g

Saturated Fat: 2g

Cholesterol: 0mg

Sodium: 600mg

Total Carbohydrates: 75g

Dietary Fiber: 15g

Sugars: 5g

Protein: 20g

Tuna Salad Wraps with Whole-Wheat Tortillas and Vegetables

Ingredients:

- Two drained cans of tuna (5 ounces each) in water
- 1/4 cup Greek yogurt
- 1 tablespoon lemon juice
- 1/4 cup finely chopped celery
- 1/4 cup finely chopped red bell pepper
- 2 tablespoons chopped fresh parsley
- Salt and pepper to taste
- 2 whole-wheat tortillas
- Lettuce leaves, sliced cucumber, and shredded carrots for filling

Preparation Method:

- In a bowl, combine the drained tuna, Greek yogurt, lemon juice, chopped celery, chopped red bell pepper, chopped parsley, salt, and pepper. Mix until well combined.

- Lay out the whole-wheat tortillas and divide the tuna salad mixture evenly between them, spreading it out in the center of each tortilla.
- Top each tortilla with lettuce leaves, sliced cucumber, and shredded carrots.
- Roll up the tortillas tightly to form wraps.
- Slice each wrap in half diagonally and serve immediately, or wrap them in foil for later enjoyment.
- Serve cold or at room temperature and enjoy!

Serving Size: 2 servings

Nutritional Information (per serving):

Calories: 300

Total Fat: 6g

Saturated Fat: 1g

Cholesterol: 30mg

Sodium: 600mg

Total Carbohydrates: 30g

Dietary Fiber: 5g

Sugars: 5g

Protein: 30g

Quinoa Salad with Herbs and Lemon:

Ingredients:
- 1 cup quinoa
- 2 cups water or low-sodium vegetable broth
- 1/4 cup fresh parsley, chopped
- 1/4 cup fresh cilantro, chopped
- 1/4 cup fresh mint, chopped
- 1/4 cup green onions, thinly sliced
- 2 tablespoons lemon juice
- 2 tablespoons extra virgin olive oil
- Salt and pepper, to taste

Preparation Method:
- Rinse the quinoa under cold water.
- In a medium saucepan, bring water or vegetable broth to a boil.
- Add the quinoa to the boiling liquid, reduce heat to low, cover, and simmer for 15-20 minutes, or until the quinoa is tender and the liquid is absorbed.
- Using a fork, fluff the quinoa before adding it to a larger mixing basin.
- Add chopped parsley, cilantro, mint, green onions, lemon juice, olive oil, salt, and pepper to the quinoa. Mix well to combine.
- Adjust seasoning to taste and serve the quinoa salad chilled or at room temperature.

Serving Size: 4 servings
Nutritional Information (per serving):
Calories: 220
Total Fat: 7g
Saturated Fat: 1g
Cholesterol: 0mg
Sodium: 10mg
Total Carbohydrates: 33g
Dietary Fiber: 4g
Sugars: 0g
Protein: 6g

Turkey Meatballs with Marinara Sauce and Zucchini Noodles:

Ingredients:
- 1 lb. lean ground turkey
- 1/4 cup almond flour
- 1/4 cup grated Parmesan cheese
- 1 egg
- 2 cloves garlic, minced
- 1 teaspoon dried oregano
- 1 teaspoon dried basil
- Salt and pepper, to taste
- 2 cups marinara sauce (look for low-sodium and no added sugar varieties)
- 4 medium zucchinis, spiralized into noodles
- Fresh basil leaves, for garnish

Preparation Method:
- In a large mixing bowl, combine ground turkey, almond flour, Parmesan cheese, egg, minced garlic, dried oregano, dried basil, salt, and pepper. Mix until well combined.
- Roll the turkey mixture into meatballs, about 1 inch in diameter.

- In a skillet over medium heat, cook the meatballs for 8-10 minutes, or until browned on all sides and cooked through.
- Meanwhile, heat the marinara sauce in a separate saucepan until warmed through.
- In another skillet, lightly sauté the zucchini noodles until just tender.
- To serve, place zucchini noodles on plates, top with meatballs, and spoon marinara sauce over the meatballs. Garnish with fresh basil leaves.

Serving Size: 4 servings
Nutritional Information (per serving):
Calories: 280
Total Fat: 12g
Saturated Fat: 3g
Cholesterol: 105mg
Sodium: 450mg
Total Carbohydrates: 14g
Dietary Fiber: 4g
Sugars: 8g
Protein: 28g

Greek Yogurt Bowl with Berries, Nuts, and Chia Seeds:

Ingredients:
- 2 cups Greek yogurt (unsweetened)
- One cup of mixed berries, including raspberries, blueberries, and strawberries
- 1/4 cup of mixed nuts, including walnuts and almonds
- 2 tablespoons chia seeds
- 1 tablespoon honey or a natural sweetener of choice (optional)

Preparation Method:
- Divide the Greek yogurt evenly into serving bowls.
- Top each bowl of yogurt with mixed berries, mixed nuts, and chia seeds.
- Drizzle honey or a natural sweetener over the yogurt if desired.
- Serve immediately and enjoy as a nutritious and satisfying lunch option.

Serving Size: 2 servings
Nutritional Information (per serving):
Calories: 250
Total Fat: 12g
Saturated Fat: 2g

Cholesterol: 10mg
Sodium: 50mg
Total Carbohydrates: 18g
Dietary Fiber: 5g
Sugars: 9g
Protein: 20g

Lentil and Vegetable Curry:

Ingredients:

- 1 cup dry green or brown lentils
- 2 cups low-sodium vegetable broth
- 1 tablespoon olive oil
- 1 onion, diced
- 2 cloves garlic, minced
- 1 tablespoon curry powder
- 1 teaspoon ground cumin
- 1/2 teaspoon ground turmeric
- 1/4 teaspoon cayenne pepper (optional)
- 1 can (14 ounces) diced tomatoes, undrained
- Two cups of mixed veggies, including cauliflower, carrots, and bell peppers
- Salt and pepper, to taste
- Fresh cilantro, for garnish (optional)

Preparation Method:

- Rinse the lentils under cold water and drain.
- Olive oil should be heated over medium heat in a big saucepan.
- Add diced onion and minced garlic, sauté until softened.
- Stir in curry powder, cumin, turmeric, and cayenne pepper (if using), and cook for another minute until fragrant.
- Add diced tomatoes, lentils, and vegetable broth to the saucepan. Bring to a boil, then reduce heat to low, cover, and simmer for about 20-25 minutes, or until lentils are tender.
- Add mixed vegetables to the lentil mixture and simmer for an additional 10 minutes, or until vegetables are cooked through.
- Season with salt and pepper to taste. Garnish with fresh cilantro if desired.
- Serve hot, either on its own or with a side of cauliflower rice or whole grain bread.

Serving Size: 4 servings
Nutritional Information (per serving):
Calories: 250
Total Fat: 4g
Saturated Fat: 0.5g
Cholesterol: 0mg
Sodium: 350mg
Total Carbohydrates: 40g
Dietary Fiber: 15g
Sugars: 6g
Protein: 15g

Chapter 3:

Dinnertime Feasts:

Slow-Cooker Turkey Chili with Kidney Beans and Corn:

Ingredients:

- 1 lb. lean ground turkey
- One can (15 oz) of washed and drained kidney beans
- 1 cup frozen corn kernels
- 1 can (15 oz) diced tomatoes, with juices
- 1 onion, chopped
- 2 cloves garlic, minced
- 1 tablespoon chili powder
- 1 teaspoon ground cumin
- 1/2 teaspoon paprika
- Salt and pepper to taste

- Optional toppings: Greek yogurt, chopped green onions, cilantro

Preparation Method:
- Cook the ground turkey in a pan over a medium-high flame until browned. If needed, drain the extra fat.
- After cooking, place the turkey in a slow cooker. Add the corn, chopped tomatoes, chili powder, cumin, paprika, onion, garlic, kidney beans, and salt and pepper. Mix everything together.
- Cook, covered, for 6–8 hours on low heat or 3–4 hours on high heat.
- If desired, top hot dish with optional garnishes.

Serving Size: 6 servings

Nutritional Information (per serving):

Calories: 250

Total Fat: 5g

Saturated Fat: 1g

Cholesterol: 40mg

Sodium: 500mg

Total Carbohydrates: 25g

Dietary Fiber: 7g

Sugars: 5g

Protein: 25g

Baked Salmon with Herb Crust and Roasted Asparagus:

Ingredients:
- 4 salmon fillets (4-6 oz each)
- 1/4 cup almond flour
- 2 tablespoons chopped fresh herbs (such as parsley, dill, or thyme)
- 1 tablespoon olive oil
- Salt and pepper to taste
- 1 bunch asparagus, trimmed
- 1 tablespoon lemon juice

Preparation Method:
- Preheat the oven to 400°F (200°C). Line a baking sheet with parchment paper.
- In a small bowl, mix together the almond flour, chopped fresh herbs, olive oil, salt, and pepper.
- After the baking sheet is ready, put the salmon fillets on it. Place a small amount of the herb crust mixture on each fillet.

- Place the asparagus on the baking sheet next to the salmon. Sprinkle with a little pepper and salt and drizzle with lemon juice.
- Bake for between twelve and fifteen minutes, or until the asparagus is soft and the salmon is cooked through, in a preheated oven.
- Serve hot.

Serving Size: 4 servings

Nutritional Information (per serving):

Calories: 300

Total Fat: 15g

Saturated Fat: 2g

Cholesterol: 75mg

Sodium: 250mg

Total Carbohydrates: 7g

Dietary Fiber: 3g

Sugars: 2g

Protein: 30g

Chicken Stir-Fry with Vegetables and Brown Rice:

Ingredients:

- 1 lb. boneless, skinless chicken breast, thinly sliced
- 2 tablespoons low-sodium soy sauce
- 1 tablespoon olive oil
- 2 cloves garlic, minced
- 1 teaspoon grated ginger
- 1 bell pepper, sliced
- 1 cup broccoli florets
- 1 cup sliced mushrooms
- 1 cup snow peas
- 2 cups cooked brown rice
- Salt and pepper to taste
- Optional toppings: sliced green onions, sesame seeds

Preparation Method:

- In a bowl, marinate the sliced chicken breast in soy sauce for about 15 minutes.
- On medium-high heat, warm up the olive oil in a big skillet or wok. Cook for approximately a minute, or until aromatic, after adding the minced garlic and grated ginger.
- Cook the chicken that has been marinated for 5 to 7 minutes, or until it is browned and cooked through.
- Add the bell pepper, broccoli, mushrooms, and snow peas to the skillet. Stir-fry for another 5 minutes until the vegetables are tender-crisp.
- Season with salt and pepper to taste.
- Serve the chicken stir-fry over cooked brown rice.
- Garnish with optional toppings like sliced green onions and sesame seeds if desired.

Serving Size: 4 servings

Nutritional Information (per serving):

Calories: 300

Total Fat: 7g

Saturated Fat: 1g

Cholesterol: 75mg

Sodium: 300mg

Total Carbohydrates: 25g

Dietary Fiber: 5g

Sugars: 3g

Protein: 30g

Vegetarian Chili with Tofu, Black Beans, and Quinoa:

Ingredients:

- 1 block (14 oz) firm tofu, drained and cubed
- One can (15 oz) of rinsed and drained black beans
- One 14-oz can have chopped tomatoes with juice
- 1 cup cooked quinoa
- 1 onion, chopped
- 2 cloves garlic, minced
- 1 bell pepper, chopped
- 1 tablespoon chili powder
- 1 teaspoon ground cumin
- 1/2 teaspoon paprika
- Salt and pepper to taste
- Optional toppings: diced avocado, chopped cilantro, lime wedges

Preparation Method:

- Warm up the olive oil in a big pot over a medium-high flame.
- Add chopped onion and minced garlic, and sauté until softened, about 3-4 minutes.
- Add cubed tofu to the pot and cook until lightly browned, about 5 minutes.
- Stir in chopped bell pepper, chili powder, cumin, paprika, salt, and pepper. Cook for another 2 minutes.
- Add diced tomatoes, black beans, and cooked quinoa to the pot. Stir to combine.
- Bring the chili to a simmer, then reduce heat to low and let it cook for 20-25 minutes, stirring occasionally.
- Finally, if wanted, top the heated dish with additional toppings.

Serving Size: 6 servings

Nutritional Information (per serving):

Calories: 250

Total Fat: 8g

Saturated Fat: 1g

Cholesterol: 0mg

Sodium: 400mg

Total Carbohydrates: 30g

Dietary Fiber: 8g

Sugars: 3g

Protein: 15g

Lentil Shepherd's Pie with Cauliflower Mash:

Ingredients:

- 1 cup dry green or brown lentils
- 2 cups vegetable broth
- 1 onion, chopped
- 2 cloves garlic, minced
- 1 carrot, diced
- 1 cup frozen mixed vegetables (corn, peas, carrots)
- 1 tablespoon tomato paste
- 1 teaspoon dried thyme
- Salt and pepper to taste
- 1 head cauliflower, cut into florets
- 1/4 cup unsweetened almond milk
- 2 tablespoons nutritional yeast (optional)
- Fresh parsley for garnish

Preparation Method:

- In a large pot, combine dry lentils and vegetable broth. Once the lentils are soft, bring to a boil, then lower the heat and simmer for 20 to 25 minutes.
- Olive oil should be heated over medium heat in a different skillet.
- Add chopped onion, minced garlic, and diced carrot. Sauté until softened, about 5 minutes.
- Add frozen mixed vegetables, tomato paste, dried thyme, salt, and pepper to the skillet. Cook for another 5 minutes.
- Preheat the oven to 375°F (190°C).
- In a large bowl, steam cauliflower florets until tender. Drain excess water, then mash cauliflower with a potato masher or fork.
- Stir in almond milk and nutritional yeast into the mashed cauliflower until smooth and creamy.
- In a baking dish, spread cooked lentils evenly on the bottom. Top with the vegetable mixture.
- Spread the mashed cauliflower over the vegetables, covering them completely.
- Bake in the preheated oven for 20-25 minutes, or until the top is lightly golden.
- Serve hot, garnished with fresh parsley.

Serving Size: 6 servings

Nutritional Information (per serving):

Calories: 200

Total Fat: 2g

Saturated Fat: 0g

Cholesterol: 0mg

Sodium: 300mg

Total Carbohydrates: 35g

Dietary Fiber: 10g

Sugars: 5g

Protein: 12g

Baked Chicken with Roasted Vegetables:

Ingredients:
- 4 boneless, skinless chicken breasts
- 2 cups mixed vegetables (such as bell peppers, broccoli, and cauliflower)
- 2 tablespoons olive oil
- 2 cloves garlic, minced
- 1 teaspoon dried thyme
- Salt and pepper, to taste

Preparation Method:
- Preheat the oven to 400°F (200°C).

- Place the chicken breasts and mixed vegetables on a baking sheet lined with parchment paper.
- Olive oil, dried thyme, minced garlic, salt, and pepper should all be combined in a small bowl.
- Drizzle the olive oil mixture over the chicken and vegetables, ensuring they are evenly coated.
- Bake in the preheated oven for 25-30 minutes, or until the chicken is cooked through and the vegetables are tender.
- Serve hot and enjoy!

Serving Size: 1 chicken breast with vegetables
Nutritional Information (per serving):

Calories: 300
Total Fat: 12g
Saturated Fat: 2g
Cholesterol: 80mg
Sodium: 250mg
Total Carbohydrates: 10g
Dietary Fiber: 3g
Sugars: 4g
Protein: 35g

Shrimp Scampi with Zucchini Noodles:

Ingredients:
- 1-pound large shrimp, peeled and deveined
- 4 medium zucchinis, spiralized into noodles
- 3 tablespoons olive oil

- 4 cloves garlic, minced
- 1/4 cup chicken broth
- Juice of 1 lemon
- 2 tablespoons chopped fresh parsley
- Salt and pepper, to taste

Preparation Method:

- The olive oil should be heated over medium heat in a big skillet. Once aromatic, add the minced garlic and simmer for one minute.
- Cook the shrimp in the skillet for two to three minutes on each side, or until they turn pink and become opaque.
- After removing them from the skillet, set the shrimp aside.
- Pour the chicken stock and lemon juice into the same skillet. Raise to a simmer.
- Cook the zucchini noodles in the skillet for two to three minutes, or until they are soft.
- Return the cooked shrimp to the skillet and toss everything together.
- Season with salt, pepper, and chopped parsley.
- Serve hot and enjoy!

Serving Size: 1/4 of the recipe
Nutritional Information (per serving):

Calories: 250
Total Fat: 12g
Saturated Fat: 2g
Cholesterol: 200mg
Sodium: 350mg
Total Carbohydrates: 10g
Dietary Fiber: 3g
Sugars: 4g
Protein: 30g

Turkey Meatloaf with Roasted Vegetables:

Ingredients:

- 1-pound lean ground turkey
- 1/2 cup almond flour
- 1/4 cup unsweetened almond milk
- 1 egg
- 1/4 cup chopped onion
- 1 clove garlic, minced
- 1 teaspoon dried thyme
- 1 teaspoon dried oregano
- Salt and pepper, to taste
- 2 cups mixed vegetables (such as carrots, bell peppers, and Brussels sprouts)
- 2 tablespoons olive oil

Preparation Method:

- Preheat the oven to 375°F (190°C).
- In a large bowl, combine the ground turkey, almond flour, almond milk, egg, chopped onion, minced garlic, dried thyme, dried oregano, salt, and pepper. Mix until well combined.
- Form the turkey mixture into a loaf shape and place it on a baking sheet lined with parchment paper.

- In a separate bowl, toss the mixed vegetables with olive oil, salt, and pepper.
- Arrange the vegetables around the turkey meatloaf on the baking sheet.
- Bake in the preheated oven for 45-50 minutes, or until the meatloaf is cooked through and the vegetables are tender.
- Serve hot and enjoy!

Serving Size: 1/4 of the meatloaf with vegetables
Nutritional Information (per serving):
Calories: 300
Total Fat: 15g
Saturated Fat: 3g
Cholesterol: 100mg
Sodium: 350mg
Total Carbohydrates: 15g
Dietary Fiber: 5g
Sugars: 4g
Protein: 30g

Black Bean Burgers with Sweet Potato Fries:

Ingredients:
- After cooking, drain and rinse two cups of black beans.

- 1/2 cup almond flour
- 1/4 cup chopped onion
- 1 clove garlic, minced
- 1 teaspoon ground cumin
- 1/2 teaspoon chili powder
- Salt and pepper, to taste
- 2 tablespoons olive oil
- 2 medium sweet potatoes, cut into fries

Preparation Method:

- Preheat the oven to 400°F (200°C).
- In a food processor, combine the black beans, almond flour, chopped onion, minced garlic, ground cumin, chili powder, salt, and pepper. Pulse the mixture until it's well blended and still has some chunks.
- Patties should be formed from the bean mixture.
- The olive oil should be heated over a moderate temperature in a big skillet.
- Cook the bean burgers for 3-4 minutes on each side, until golden brown.
- Transfer the bean burgers to a baking sheet lined with parchment paper.
- Place the sweet potato fries on the same baking sheet.
- Bake in the preheated oven for 20-25 minutes, flipping the fries halfway through, until the burgers are heated through and the fries are crispy.
- Serve the black bean burgers with the sweet potato fries and enjoy!

Serving Size: 1 burger patty with sweet potato fries

Nutritional Information (per serving):

Calories: 300

Total Fat: 10g

Saturated Fat: 2g

Cholesterol: 0mg
Sodium: 350mg
Total Carbohydrates: 40g
Dietary Fiber: 10g
Sugars: 5g
Protein: 15g

Salmon with Lemon and Dill:

Ingredients:
- 4 salmon fillets
- 2 tablespoons olive oil
- Juice of 1 lemon
- 2 cloves garlic, minced
- 2 tablespoons chopped fresh dill
- Salt and pepper, to taste
- Lemon slices, for garnish

Preparation Method:
- Warm the oven up to 400°F, or 200°C.
- The salmon fillets should be placed on a parchment paper-lined baking pan.
- Mix the olive oil, lemon juice, minced garlic, chopped fresh dill, salt, and pepper in a small bowl.

- Making sure the salmon fillets are evenly covered, drizzle the olive oil mixture over them.
- As a garnish, place a slice of lemon over each fillet of salmon.
- The salmon should flake easily with a fork after 12 to 15 minutes of baking in a preheated oven.
- Serve hot and enjoy!

Serving Size: 1 salmon fillet
Nutritional Information (per serving):
Calories: 300
Total Fat: 15g
Saturated Fat: 2g
Cholesterol: 80mg
Sodium: 350mg
Total Carbohydrates: 2g
Dietary Fiber: 0g
Sugars: 0g
Protein: 35g

CHAPTER 4:

Satisfying Snacks:

Spiced Roasted Chickpeas

Ingredients:

- One 15-oz can have washed and drained chickpeas
- 1 tablespoon olive oil
- 1 teaspoon ground cumin
- 1/2 teaspoon smoked paprika
- 1/2 teaspoon garlic powder
- 1/4 teaspoon cayenne pepper
- Salt to taste

Preparation Method:

- Adjust the oven temperature to 400 degrees Fahrenheit (200 degrees Celsius) and place parchment paper on a baking pan.
- Using a paper towel, pat dry the chickpeas and remove any loose skins.
- Toss the chickpeas in a bowl with salt, garlic powder, cayenne pepper, cumin, smoked paprika, and olive oil until well covered.
- Arrange the chickpeas on the baking sheet that has been preheated in a single layer.
- Roast for roughly twenty to twenty-five minutes in an already heated oven, stirring the pan halfway through, or until the food is crispy and has a golden-brown hue.
- Before serving, take out of the oven and allow it cool.

Serving Size: 1/4 cup

Nutritional Information (per serving):

Calories: 90

Total Fat: 3g

Saturated Fat: 0g

Cholesterol: 0mg

Sodium: 140mg

Total Carbohydrates: 13g

Dietary Fiber: 4g

Sugars: 0g

Protein: 4g

Avocado and Cucumber Roll-Ups

Ingredients:

- 1 large cucumber
- 1 ripe avocado
- Juice of 1/2 lemon
- Salt and pepper to taste
- If desired, fresh herbs (such basil or cilantro)

Preparation Method:

- Using a vegetable peeler, slice the cucumber lengthwise into thin strips.
- Avocado, lemon juice, salt, and pepper should be mashed in a basin.
- Drizzle each cucumber strip with a little amount of mashed avocado.
- Roll up the cucumber strips, securing with toothpicks if necessary.
- Optional: Garnish with fresh herbs before serving.

Serving Size: 2 roll-ups

Nutritional Information (per serving):

Calories: 90

Total Fat: 7g

Saturated Fat: 1g

Cholesterol: 0mg

Sodium: 5mg

Total Carbohydrates: 7g

Dietary Fiber: 4g

Sugars: 1g

Protein: 2g

Greek Yogurt Dip with Vegetable Dippers

Ingredients:

- 1 cup plain Greek yogurt (low-fat or non-fat)
- 1 clove garlic, minced
- 1 tablespoon lemon juice
- 1 tablespoon chopped fresh dill
- Salt and pepper to taste

- Assorted vegetable dippers (such as carrot sticks, cucumber slices, bell pepper strips)

Preparation Method:

- In a bowl, mix together Greek yogurt, minced garlic, lemon juice, chopped dill, salt, and pepper.
- Adjust seasoning to taste.
- Serve the Greek yogurt dip with assorted vegetable dippers.

Serving Size: 2 tablespoons dip with vegetables

Nutritional Information (per serving):

Calories: 30

Total Fat: 0g

Saturated Fat: 0g

Cholesterol: 0mg

Sodium: 20mg

Total Carbohydrates: 3g

Dietary Fiber: 0g

Sugars: 2g

Protein: 4g

Apple Slices with Almond Butter

Ingredients:

- 1 medium apple, sliced
- 2 tablespoons almond butter

Preparation Method:

- Slice the apple into wedges or rings.
- Serve with almond butter for dipping.

Serving Size: 1 medium apple with 2 tablespoons almond butter

Nutritional Information (per serving):

Calories: 220

Total Fat: 14g

Saturated Fat: 1g

Cholesterol: 0mg

Sodium: 0mg

Total Carbohydrates: 24g

Dietary Fiber: 5g

Sugars: 15g

Protein: 5g

Chia Seed Pudding Cups

Ingredients:

- 1/4 cup chia seeds
- 1 cup unsweetened almond milk
- 1 tablespoon unsweetened cocoa powder
- 1 tablespoon natural sweetener (such as stevia or monk fruit extract)
- 1/4 teaspoon vanilla extract
- Optional toppings: Fresh berries, sliced almonds, shredded coconut

Preparation Method:

- In a bowl, whisk together chia seeds, almond milk, cocoa powder, natural sweetener, and vanilla extract.
- To avoid clumping, give the mixture five minutes to settle before whisking it once more.
- Cover and refrigerate for at least 2 hours or overnight, until thickened.

- Divide the chia seed pudding into individual cups and top with optional toppings before serving.

Serving Size: 1/2 cup pudding

Nutritional Information (per serving):

Calories: 120

Total Fat: 7g

Saturated Fat: 0.5g

Cholesterol: 0mg

Sodium: 80mg

Total Carbohydrates: 13g

Dietary Fiber: 9g

Sugars: 1g

Protein: 4g

Hard-Boiled Eggs with Avocado Hummus

Ingredients:

- 4 large eggs
- 1 ripe avocado
- Juice of 1/2 lemon
- 1 clove garlic, minced
- Salt and pepper to taste

Preparation Method:

- Put the eggs into a pot and pour water over them. After bringing to a boil, lower heat, and simmer for ten minutes.
- After draining, run the eggs under cold water to chill. Peel and halve the eggs.
- In a bowl, mash the avocado with lemon juice, minced garlic, salt, and pepper to make avocado hummus.

- Serve the hard-boiled eggs with avocado hummus.

Serving Size: 2 eggs with avocado hummus

Nutritional Information (per serving):

Calories: 220

Total Fat: 16g

Saturated Fat: 3g

Cholesterol: 370mg

Sodium: 170mg

Total Carbohydrates: 9g

Dietary Fiber: 6g

Sugars: 1g

Protein: 13g

14 DAYS MEAL PLAN

Day 1:

Breakfast:

Chia Pudding with Berries and Nuts

Lunch:

Salmon Salad with Quinoa and Roasted Vegetables

Dinner:

Baked Chicken with Roasted Vegetables

Snacks:

Spiced Roasted Chickpeas, Carrot Sticks with Hummus

Day 2:

Breakfast:

Scrambled Eggs with Smoked Salmon and Avocado

Lunch:

Black Bean Burgers on Whole-Wheat Buns with Sweet Potato Fries

Dinner:

Lentil Shepherd's Pie with Cauliflower Mash

Snacks:

Apple Slices with Almond Butter, Greek Yogurt Dip with Vegetable Dippers

Day 3:

Breakfast:

Whole-Wheat Pancakes with Berries and Greek Yogurt

Lunch:

Chicken Caesar Salad with Greek Yogurt Dressing

Dinner:

Slow-Cooker Turkey Chili with Kidney Beans and Corn

Snacks:

Hard-Boiled Eggs with Avocado Hummus, Edamame and Seaweed Snacks

Day 4:

Breakfast:

Oatmeal with Chia Seeds and Sliced Almonds

Lunch:

Tuna Salad Wraps with Whole-Wheat Tortillas and Vegetables

Dinner:

Shrimp Scampi with Zucchini Noodles

Snacks:

Sliced Bell Peppers with Cottage Cheese, Celery Sticks with Peanut Butter

Day 5:

Breakfast:

Avocado Toast with Scrambled Eggs

Lunch:

Lentil Soup with Whole-Wheat Bread

Dinner:

Turkey Meatloaf with Roasted Vegetables

Snacks:

Pear with String Cheese, Roasted Almonds and Walnuts

Day 6:

Breakfast:

Omelets with Spinach, Feta, and Tomato

Lunch:

Leftover Salmon Salad Sandwich on Whole-Wheat Bread

Dinner:

Vegetarian Chili with Tofu, Black Beans, and Quinoa

Snacks:

Cottage Cheese with Pineapple Chunks, Air-Fried Zucchini Chips with Parmesan Cheese

Day 7:

Breakfast:

Smoothie Bowl with Spinach, Banana, and Almond Milk

Lunch:

Greek Yogurt Bowl with Berries, Nuts, and Chia Seeds

Dinner:

Baked Salmon with Herb Crust and Roasted Asparagus

Snacks:

Cucumber Slices with Smoked Salmon, Mini Bell Pepper Boats with Guacamole

Day 8:

Breakfast:

Baked Egg Muffins with Vegetables

Lunch:

Quinoa Salad with Herbs and Lemon

Dinner:

Chicken Stir-Fry with Vegetables and Brown Rice

Snacks:

Spiced Roasted Chickpeas, Apple Slices with Almond Butter

Day 9:

Breakfast:

Chia Pudding with Berries and Nuts

Lunch:

Black Bean Burgers on Whole-Wheat Buns with Sweet Potato Fries

Dinner:

Lentil Shepherd's Pie with Cauliflower Mash

Snacks:

Hard-Boiled Eggs with Avocado Hummus, Edamame and Seaweed Snacks

Day 10:

Breakfast:

Scrambled Eggs with Smoked Salmon and Avocado

Lunch:

Chicken Caesar Salad with Greek Yogurt Dressing

Dinner:

Slow-Cooker Turkey Chili with Kidney Beans and Corn

Snacks:

Sliced Bell Peppers with Cottage Cheese, Celery Sticks with Peanut Butter

Day 11:

Breakfast:

Whole-Wheat Pancakes with Berries and Greek Yogurt

Lunch:

Tuna Salad Wraps with Whole-Wheat Tortillas and Vegetables

Dinner:

Shrimp Scampi with Zucchini Noodles

Snacks:

Pear with String Cheese, Roasted Almonds and Walnuts

Day 12:

Breakfast:

Avocado Toast with Scrambled Eggs

Lunch:

Lentil Soup with Whole-Wheat Bread

Dinner:

Turkey Meatloaf with Roasted Vegetables

Snacks:

Cottage Cheese with Pineapple Chunks, Air-Fried Zucchini Chips with Parmesan Cheese

Day 13:

Breakfast:
Omelets with Spinach, Feta, and Tomato

Lunch:
Leftover Salmon Salad Sandwich on Whole-Wheat Bread

Dinner:
Vegetarian Chili with Tofu, Black Beans, and Quinoa

Snacks:
Cucumber Slices with Smoked Salmon, Mini Bell Pepper Boats with Guacamole

Day 14:

Breakfast:

Smoothie Bowl with Spinach, Banana, and Almond Milk

Lunch:

Greek Yogurt Bowl with Berries, Nuts, and Chia Seeds

Dinner:

Baked Salmon with Herb Crust and Roasted Asparagus

CONCLUSION

Congratulations! You've embarked on a delicious journey, navigating the world of flavor while managing your diabetes and cholesterol.

This cookbook was your companion, offering delectable recipes and guidance, but remember, the true adventure lies beyond these pages.

You now possess the knowledge to explore new ingredients, experiment with cooking techniques, and tailor dishes to your unique preferences.

Don't be afraid to get creative! Substitute, swap, and play with flavors to discover hidden gems that fit your palate and health goals.

Remember, this isn't just about following recipes; it's about empowering yourself to cook with confidence and enjoyment.

As you progress, remember that managing health is a marathon, not a sprint.
There will be easy days and difficult ones. Indulge occasionally, but don't let setbacks derail your progress. Embrace healthy habits as a lifestyle, not just a temporary fix.

Celebrate your victories, learn from slip-ups, and most importantly, enjoy the journey!

This cookbook may close, but your culinary adventure continues. Keep exploring, keep learning, and keep savoring the delicious possibilities that lie ahead. Never forget that eating well doesn't have to be boring or limited.
It's a vibrant tapestry woven with flavor, mindful choices, and the joy of cooking. So, keep experimenting, keep sharing meals with loved ones, and keep reminding yourself that every delicious bite is a step towards a healthier, happier you

Made in the USA
Las Vegas, NV
20 October 2024